Madeleine Floyd

Born in 1969, Madeleine Floyd studied Fine
Art and Illustration at Camberwell College of
Art, London, and has achieved great success in
both fields. Her illustrations, watercolours and
oil paintings are well known and have been
published and collected around the world. She
works from her garden studio in London and
has become one of Britain's best-loved artists.
A long-standing appreciation of nature led to
Madeleine producing a sketchbook full
of Birdsong illustrations and this has since
grown into a successful range of beautiful
licensed products.

Madeleine Floyd

A Year of Birdsong
2014 DIARY

" Chit - chit - chiti - tzerrr........" Wren

Personal Details

Name

Address

Telephone: Home

Mobile

Work

E-mail

In emergency please contact:

Telephone

Useful Information

National Insurance no.

Driving licence no.

AA/RAC no.

Other Useful Numbers

Doctor	Dentist
Optician	Childminder
School	Vet
Bank	Building society
Train station	Bus station
Airport	Water
Plumber	Electrician
Gas	Electricity
Hairdresser	Garage
Taxi	Cinema

2014 Calendar

JANUARY
```
M  ·   6  13  20  27
T  ·   7  14  21  28
W  1   8  15  22  29
T  2   9  16  23  30
F  3  10  17  24  31
S  4  11  18  25   ·
S  5  12  19  26   ·
```

FEBRUARY
```
M  ·   3  10  17  24
T  ·   4  11  18  25
W  ·   5  12  19  26
T  ·   6  13  20  27
F  ·   7  14  21  28
S  1   8  15  22   ·
S  2   9  16  23   ·
```

MARCH
```
M  31   3  10  17  24
T   ·   4  11  18  25
W   ·   5  12  19  26
T   ·   6  13  20  27
F   ·   7  14  21  28
S   1   8  15  22  29
S   2   9  16  23  30
```

APRIL
```
M  ·   7  14  21  28
T  1   8  15  22  29
W  2   9  16  23  30
T  3  10  17  24   ·
F  4  11  18  25   ·
S  5  12  19  26   ·
S  6  13  20  27   ·
```

MAY
```
M  ·   5  12  19  26
T  ·   6  13  20  27
W  ·   7  14  21  28
T  1   8  15  22  29
F  2   9  16  23  30
S  3  10  17  24  31
S  4  11  18  25   ·
```

JUNE
```
M  30   2   9  16  23
T   ·   3  10  17  24
W   ·   4  11  18  25
T   ·   5  12  19  26
F   ·   6  13  20  27
S   ·   7  14  21  28
S   1   8  15  22  29
```

JULY
```
M  ·   7  14  21  28
T  1   8  15  22  29
W  2   9  16  23  30
T  3  10  17  24  31
F  4  11  18  25   ·
S  5  12  19  26   ·
S  6  13  20  27   ·
```

AUGUST
```
M  ·   4  11  18  25
T  ·   5  12  19  26
W  ·   6  13  20  27
T  ·   7  14  21  28
F  1   8  15  22  29
S  2   9  16  23  30
S  3  10  17  24  31
```

SEPTEMBER
```
M  1   8  15  22  29
T  2   9  16  23  30
W  3  10  17  24   ·
T  4  11  18  25   ·
F  5  12  19  26   ·
S  6  13  20  27   ·
S  7  14  21  28   ·
```

OCTOBER
```
M  ·   6  13  20  27
T  ·   7  14  21  28
W  1   8  15  22  29
T  2   9  16  23  30
F  3  10  17  24  31
S  4  11  18  25   ·
S  5  12  19  26   ·
```

NOVEMBER
```
M  ·   3  10  17  24
T  ·   4  11  18  25
W  ·   5  12  19  26
T  ·   6  13  20  27
F  ·   7  14  21  28
S  1   8  15  22  29
S  2   9  16  23  30
```

DECEMBER
```
M  1   8  15  22  29
T  2   9  16  23  30
W  3  10  17  24  31
T  4  11  18  25   ·
F  5  12  19  26   ·
S  6  13  20  27   ·
S  7  14  21  28   ·
```

2015 Calendar

JANUARY
```
M  ·   5  12  19  26
T  ·   6  13  20  27
W  ·   7  14  21  28
T  1   8  15  22  29
F  2   9  16  23  30
S  3  10  17  24  31
S  4  11  18  25   ·
```

FEBRUARY
```
M  ·   2   9  16  23
T  ·   3  10  17  24
W  ·   4  11  18  25
T  ·   5  12  19  26
F  ·   6  13  20  27
S  ·   7  14  21  28
S  1   8  15  22   ·
```

MARCH
```
M  30   2   9  16  23
T  31   3  10  17  24
W   ·   4  11  18  25
T   ·   5  12  19  26
F   ·   6  13  20  27
S   ·   7  14  21  28
S   1   8  15  22  29
```

APRIL
```
M  ·   6  13  20  27
T  ·   7  14  21  28
W  1   8  15  22  29
T  2   9  16  23  30
F  3  10  17  24   ·
S  4  11  18  25   ·
S  5  12  19  26   ·
```

MAY
```
M  ·   4  11  18  25
T  ·   5  12  19  26
W  ·   6  13  20  27
T  ·   7  14  21  28
F  1   8  15  22  29
S  2   9  16  23  30
S  3  10  17  24  31
```

JUNE
```
M  1   8  15  22  29
T  2   9  16  23  30
W  3  10  17  24   ·
T  4  11  18  25   ·
F  5  12  19  26   ·
S  6  13  20  27   ·
S  7  14  21  28   ·
```

JULY
```
M  ·   6  13  20  27
T  ·   7  14  21  28
W  1   8  15  22  29
T  2   9  16  23  30
F  3  10  17  24  31
S  4  11  18  25   ·
S  5  12  19  26   ·
```

AUGUST
```
M  31   3  10  17  24
T   ·   4  11  18  25
W   ·   5  12  19  26
T   ·   6  13  20  27
F   ·   7  14  21  28
S   1   8  15  22  29
S   2   9  16  23  30
```

SEPTEMBER
```
M  ·   7  14  21  28
T  1   8  15  22  29
W  2   9  16  23  30
T  3  10  17  24   ·
F  4  11  18  25   ·
S  5  12  19  26   ·
S  6  13  20  27   ·
```

OCTOBER
```
M  ·   5  12  19  26
T  ·   6  13  20  27
W  ·   7  14  21  28
T  1   8  15  22  29
F  2   9  16  23  30
S  3  10  17  24  31
S  4  11  18  25   ·
```

NOVEMBER
```
M  30   2   9  16  23
T   ·   3  10  17  24
W   ·   4  11  18  25
T   ·   5  12  19  26
F   ·   6  13  20  27
S   ·   7  14  21  28
S   1   8  15  22  29
```

DECEMBER
```
M  ·   7  14  21  28
T  1   8  15  22  29
W  2   9  16  23  30
T  3  10  17  24  31
F  4  11  18  25   ·
S  5  12  19  26   ·
S  6  13  20  27   ·
```

December 2013

Monday
23

Tuesday
24
Christmas Eve

Wednesday
25
Christmas Day
(Holiday UK, R. of Ireland, USA, CAN, AUS, NZL)

Thursday
26
Boxing Day, St Stephen's Day
(Holiday UK, R. of Ireland, CAN, AUS, NZL)

Friday
27

Saturday
28

Sunday
29

"Ptching... tching... ..." Bearded Tit

Bearded Tit *(Panurus biarmicus)*

NOTES

"Ptching.... tching..." Bearded Tit

Bearded Tit *(Panurus biarmicus)*

Originally from East Asia, the bearded tit is a reclusive little bird who spends all his life nestled in reed beds. His voice is clear but sporadic and he often prefers silence over song, though can sometimes be heard uttering a soft, chattering verse and the odd repetitive, ringing chorus.

The bearded tit has bright yellow-ringed eyes, a soft grey head and jet-black mandarin whiskers at either side of his beak, which gave rise to his misleading name. He is a nimble fellow, hopping up and down the reed stalks. He successfully moderates his diet to accommodate insects in summer and a seed and vegetable diet in winter.

A bird came down the walk:
He did not know I saw;
He bit an angle-worm in halves
And ate the fellow, raw.
And then he drank a dew
From a convenient grass,
And then hopped sidewise to the wall
To let a beetle pass.
EMILY DICKINSON

December 2013/January 2014

Monday

30

New Year's Eve

Tuesday

31

New Year's Day (Holiday UK, R. of Ireland,
USA, CAN, AUS, NZL)

Wednesday

1

Holiday (STC, NZL)

Thursday

2

Friday

3

Saturday

4

Sunday

5

January

Monday

6

Tuesday

7

Wednesday

8

Thursday

9

Friday

10

Saturday

11

Sunday

12

"Klooo-it..... klooo-it...." Avocet

Avocet *(Recurvirostra avosetta)*

NOTES

"Klooo-it..... klooo-it..." Avocet

Avocet (*Recurvirostra avosetta*)

The avocet is an elegant bird with a clear, piped call of high-
pitched rhythmic repetitions that accelerate when alarmed.
He thrives in small colonies, largely on the east coast of
Britain, and is an inspiring success story for conservationists,
having almost become extinct in the last century. He has
an aristocratic air with black hood and wing markings
that contrast forcefully with his bright white plumage. He
can often be seen resting effortlessly on one leg and has
a remarkable narrow, upturned and elongated bill. He
sweeps this bill from side to side, sieving tiny shrimps and
invertebrates from the water to eat.

I would that we were, my beloved,
white birds on the foam of the sea!
We tire of the flame of the meteor,
before it can fade and flee;
And the flame of the blue star of twilight,
hung low on the rim of the sky,
Has awaked in our hearts, my beloved,
a sadness that may not die.
W.B. YEATS

January

Monday
13

Tuesday
14

Wednesday
15

Thursday
16

Friday
17

Saturday
18

Sunday
19

January

Monday   Martin Luther King, Jr. Day (Holiday USA)

20

Tuesday

21

Wednesday

22

Thursday

23

Friday

24

Saturday   Burns Night (SCT)

25

Sunday   Australia Day

26

"Cheeep..... cheeep....." House Sparrow

House Sparrow *(Passer domesticus)*

NOTES

"Cheeep..... cheeep....." House Sparrow

House Sparrow *(Passer domesticus)*

The native house sparrow is a bird we all know and love,
and most of us have memories of feeding these perky fellows
with crumbs at some time or other. Perhaps the fact that
they choose to nest in and around our buildings has
contributed to our affection for this bird.

The ditty of the house sparrow is persistent, lively and
chattering, consisting of much chirping and twittering as
befits this cheeky, mischievous character. Although house
sparrows remain as established couples in public, they are also
known to have illicit offspring following private infidelities!

Behold, within the leafy shade,
Those bright blue eggs together laid!
On me the chance-discovered sight
Gleamed like a vision of delight.
I started… seeming to espy
The home and sheltered bed,
The Sparrow's dwelling…
WILLIAM WORDSWORTH

January/February

Holiday (AUS)

Monday

27

Tuesday

28

Wednesday

29

Thursday

30

Friday

31

Saturday

1

Sunday

2

February

Monday

3

Tuesday

4

Wednesday

5

Thursday   Waitangi Day (Holiday NZL)

6

Friday

7

Saturday

8

Sunday

9

" chir-rr-upp.........chir-rr-uppp........." Skylark

Skylark *(Alauda arvensis)*

NOTES

"chir-rr-uppp........chir-rr-uppp........" Skylark

Skylark *(Alauda arvensis)*

Without doubt, the skylark is one of the most impressive
songbirds. Poets, artists and musicians have all been inspired
by this bird's fast, rich, high-pitched song that he belts out
with refinement and ease as he soars upward in flight before
plunging downwards, whereupon his beautifully choreographed
song ceases exactly on cue. The skylark begins practising his
fluid song as early as February and is often up before sunrise,
perfecting his melody that only improves further as the onset of
spring draws closer. Sadly the skylark is declining in numbers
owing to the increase in intensive agricultural practices, such as
the use of pesticides, which result in a lack of winter food.

Hail to thee, blithe Spirit!
Bird thou never wert –
That from Heaven or near it
Pourest thy full heart
In profuse strains of unpremeditated art.
PERCY BYSSHE SHELLEY

February

Monday
10

Tuesday
11

Wednesday
12

Thursday
13

St Valentine's Day

Friday
14

Saturday
15

Sunday
16

February

Monday	Washington's Birthday (Holiday USA)
17	

Tuesday

18

Wednesday

19

Thursday

20

Friday

21

Saturday

22

Sunday

23

"Swilt - witt - witt - witt ......" Goldfinch

Goldfinch *(Carduelis carduelis)*

NOTES

"Swilt - witt - witt - witt ....." Goldfinch

Goldfinch *(Carduelis carduelis)*

Clearly identified by his striking black and red face mask and
yellow wing bars, the goldfinch has earned his reputation
for being one of the most handsome of farmland birds
and garden visitors. A frequent and repetitive chorister,
the goldfinch has a song that is twittering and chattering
in quality with bouncing liquid trills and a confident final
flourish. The male often likes to sing near his nest and the
tone is lilting and celebratory.
Wary in character, he is hard to spot but his flight is light and
skipping with a bouncy action and, when seen travelling in
small flocks, it is an impressive sight.

Out in the sun the goldfinch flits
Along the thistle-tops, flits and twits
Above the hollow wood
Where birds swim like fish…
EDWARD THOMAS

February/March

Monday

24

Tuesday

25

Wednesday

26

Thursday

27

Friday

28

St David's Day

Saturday

1

Sunday

2

March

Monday

3

Tuesday   Shrove Tuesday

4

Wednesday

5

Thursday

6

Friday

7

Saturday

8

Sunday   Daylight Saving Time begins (CAN, USA)

9

"Charrr....charrr......" Dartford Warbler

Dartford Warbler *(Sylvia undata)*

NOTES

_____

_____

_____

_____

"Charrr.....charrr........" Dartford Warbler

Dartford Warbler *(Sylvia undata)*

Unlike his fellow warblers, the Dartford warbler braves
cold winters and remains in Britain rather than escaping to
warmer climates. As a result, this secretive and elusive bird
is susceptible to decline but he can still be found on the dry
lowland heaths of Hampshire and Dorset. His song is a
quick, chattering warble, containing some brighter notes, but
is usually sung at a fairly low pitch and often in flight.
A smart little fellow, he weighs no more than a wren, but has
an impressively long, cocked tail that is half of his overall
length. He sports a deep reddish-brown chest and a red eye
ring that looks like a rather distinguished monocle.

At half-past three a single bird
Unto a silent sky
Propounded but a single term
Of cautious melody.
At half-past four, experiment
Had subjugated test,
And lo! her silver principle
Supplanted all the rest.
EMILY DICKINSON

March

Commonwealth Day

Monday
10

Tuesday
11

Wednesday
12

Thursday
13

Friday
14

Saturday
15

Sunday
16

March

Monday

St Patrick's Day
Holiday (R. of Ireland, N. Ireland)

17

Tuesday

18

Wednesday

19

Thursday

20

Friday

21

Saturday

22

Sunday

23

"Keun-Ken-Kenk......." "Green Woodpecker

Green Woodpecker *(Picus viridis)*

NOTES

Green Woodpecker *(Picus viridis)*

The green woodpecker has a distinctive loud call and
his voice has a laughing ringing tone that has led to the
nickname of 'Yaffle' in some parts of Britain.
This suave bird sports a vivid red cap and an apple green
overcoat that make him a popular and rewarding sighting.
In flight you can also see his fine yellow rump feathers
that contribute to his dapper appearance. He prefers open
deciduous woodland and is more often seen on the ground
searching for ants with his long impressive tongue than
perched high up in the trees as one might expect.

Beside the bare and beaten track
of travelling flocks and herds
The woodpecker went tapping on,
the postman of the birds,
'I've got a letter here,' he said,
'that no one's understood,
Addressed as follows: 'To the bird
that's like a piece of wood.'
A.B. PATERSON

March

Monday
24

Tuesday
25

Wednesday
26

Thursday
27

Friday
28

Saturday
29

Mother's Day (UK, R. of Ireland)
British Summer Time begins
European Daylight Saving Time begins

Sunday
30

March/April

Monday
31

Tuesday
1

Wednesday
2

Thursday
3

Friday
4

Saturday
5

Sunday
6

Daylight Saving Time ends
(NZL, AUS – except WA, NT, QLD)

"Szeeee .... seeee .... szeee ..." Grey Wagtail

Grey Wagtail *(Motacilla cinerea)*

NOTES

_____

_____

_____

_____

"Szeeee .... seeee .... szeee ..." Grey Wagtail

Grey Wagtail *(Motacilla cinerea)*

The largely resident and elegant grey wagtail owns the
longest tail of the wagtail family and has black and smoky
grey upperparts with a sulphur yellow chest. This attractive
palette contributes to an air of a gentleman. His call can be
loud and sharp but his song is made up of chirruping flutey
notes and fast trills and warbles. He is happiest living beside a
mountain stream, enjoying the rocky terrain but can make his
home in other waterside locations as long as there is running
fresh water nearby, from which he can catch water insects
and mayflies to feast on. His flight is fast and graceful and he
lands lightly with an appropriate bobbing of his long tail.

Little Trotty Wagtail, he went in the rain
And tittering, tottering sideways,
*   he ne'er got straight again,*
He stooped to get a worm
*   and looked up to get a fly,*
And then he flew away
*   ere his feathers they were dry.*
JOHN CLARE

April

Monday

7

Tuesday

8

Wednesday

9

Thursday

10

Friday

11

Saturday

12

Sunday

13

April

Monday

14

Tuesday

15

Wednesday

16

Thursday

17

Friday   Good Friday (Holiday UK, AUS, CAN, NZL)

18

Saturday

19

Sunday   Easter Sunday

20

"Tac-tac...tac-tac..." Blackcap

Blackcap *(Sylvia atricapilla)*

NOTES

"Tac-tac...tac-tac..." Blackcap

Blackcap *(Sylvia atricapilla)*

The cheerful hymn of the blackcap, often confused with
that of the garden warbler, begins with a gentle warbling
prelude, which then accelerates in pace and volume
into an impressive bright change of key. Such musical
accomplishment has brought him the nickname 'King of the
warblers', but until recently, his vocal talent also meant that
he was a much sought-after caged bird in the Mediterranean.
This shy, migratory bird favours gardens and dense
woodlands with brambles and briars, and builds a rather
insubstantial nest that is usually found near to the ground,
hidden in bushes or undergrowth.

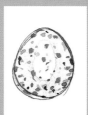

*Everyone praises, everyone cuts.
Twilight comes and they haul their
   heavy loads away.
Then, on the air, a cry —
   a blackcap in flight,
seeking a nest it will not
   find today.*
GIOVANNI PASCOLI

April

Easter Monday (Holiday UK except SCT,
R. of Ireland, CAN, AUS, NZL)

Monday

21

Earth Day

Tuesday

22

St George's Day

Wednesday

23

Thursday

24

Anzac Day (Holiday AUS, NZL)

Friday

25

Saturday

26

Sunday

27

April/May

Monday
28

Tuesday
29

Wednesday
30

Thursday
1

Friday
2

Saturday
3

Sunday
4

"Tlen-hn-hn... tlen-hu-hu......" Redshank

Redshank *(Tringa totanus)*

NOTES

_____

_____

_____

_____

"Tlen-hn-hn... tlen-hn-hn....." Redshank

Redshank *(Tringa totanus)*

One of Britain's most frequently seen waders, the redshank is notorious for his noisy and vigilant ways. He can be found across salt marshes, mud flats, wet meadows and small creeks. He is almost neurotic about protecting his eggs and fledglings and to this aim he uses resonant bouncing calls to ward off intruders. Similarly, he takes great trouble in weaving a canopy of grass above the nest to prevent eggs from being washed away by high, threatening tides. The male builds the base of the family nest, carefully positioned out of sight amongst the marshland grasses, and lets the female perfect the interior.

And all about my way were flying
The peewit, with their slow wings creaking;
And little jack-snipe darted, drumming:
And now and then a golden plover
Or redshank piped with reedy whistle.
WILFRID W. GIBSON

May

Holiday (UK, R. of Ireland)

Monday

5

Tuesday

6

Wednesday

7

Thursday

8

Friday

9

Saturday

10

Mother's Day (AUS, CAN, NZL, USA)

Sunday

11

May

Monday

12

Tuesday

13

Wednesday

14

Thursday

15

Friday

16

Saturday

17

Sunday

18

"Pi~ooooo... pi~ooooo ......" Little Ringed Plover

Little Ringed Plover *(Charadrius dubius)*

NOTES

"Pi~ooooo~ pi~oooooo ......" Little Ringed Plover

Little Ringed Plover *(Charadrius dubius)*

Usually seen busily chasing insects across coastal and river
shingle beds, the plump little ringed plover is a relative
newcomer to Britain. His call is short, abbreviated and
whistled, with a rolling tone like that of a small gull.
During their courtship display, the enamoured female shelters
under the male's outspread tail. This action is repeated,
making it appear like a coquettish dance. When threatened,
the little ringed plover wisely fluffs out his feathers in order to
present an exaggerated impression of his size and girth.
Both the male and the female look similar with a brown crown
and a distinctive black headband across their foreheads.

Had I but wings like thine,
Free bird of flight,
To scale the heights that only wings can reach,
Or steer my passage o'er yon seas of light,
Whose cloudy beach
Is ever shifting like the sands of time!
MARTHA LAVINIA HOFFMAN

May

Victoria Day (Holiday CAN)

Monday
19

Tuesday
20

Wednesday
21

Thursday
22

Friday
23

Saturday
24

Sunday
25

May/June

WEEK 22

Monday
26

Holiday (UK)
Memorial Day (Holiday USA)

Tuesday
27

Wednesday
28

Thursday
29

Friday
30

Saturday
31

Sunday
1

"Arra – arraa – arrraah" Gannet

Gannet *(Morus bassanus)*

NOTES

"Arra – arraa – arrraah" Gannet

Gannet *(Morus bassanus)*

Gannets are our largest and most striking seabird and their
huge black-tipped wings, which can reach a span of
1.8 m (6 ft), power a graceful, majestic flight that culminates in
a glide low over the water before a dive that can reach
100 km/h (60 mph). Their long pointed beaks have a spongy
bone plate at the base and their long necks have strong muscles
to lessen the impact of hitting the water.
Despite their aggressive reputation, gannet pairs are very
attentive and affectionate towards each other and stay together
for several breeding seasons.

The summer morn is bright and fresh,
The birds are darting by
As if they loved to breast the breeze
That sweeps the cool clear sky.
WILLIAM C. BRYANT

June

Holiday (R. of Ireland)
Queen's Birthday (Holiday NZL)

Monday

2

Tuesday

3

Wednesday

4

Thursday

5

Friday

6

Saturday

7

Sunday

8

June

Monday
9

Tuesday
10

Wednesday
11

Thursday
12

Friday
13

Saturday
14

Sunday   **Father's Day (UK, CAN, USA)**
15

" Turrrk - turrrk - turrrk......" Mistle Thrush

Mistle Thrush *(Turdus viscivorus)*

NOTES

"Turrrk - turrrk - turrrk......" Mistle Thrush

Mistle Thrush *(Turdus viscivorus)*

The large, bold mistle thrush is often the first to celebrate the onset of spring and, as a result, is one of Europe's most-loved songbirds. His song is long and distinctive. From the end of January, this confident migratory bird arrives at his breeding ground and is ready to perform his loud, wilful song from the top of tall conifer trees. He will happily sing through rain or dull weather and indeed often continues well into autumn. It may well be that the lofty height from which he orates, and the less favourable weather in which he chants, contribute to an overall distant quality to his far-carrying song, which has just a slight suggestion of sadness in it.

At once a voice arose among
The bleak twigs overhead
In a full-hearted evensong
Of joy illimited;
An aged thrush, frail, gaunt and small,
In blast-beruffled plume,
Had chosen thus to fling his soul
Upon the growing gloom.
THOMAS HARDY

June

Monday
16

Tuesday
17

Wednesday
18

Thursday
19

Friday
20

Saturday
21

Sunday
22

June

Monday

23

Tuesday

24

Wednesday

25

Thursday

26

Friday

27

Saturday

28

Sunday

29

"Cooo-coo-cu ...... cooo-coo-cu ...." Woodpigeon

Woodpigeon *(Columba palumbus)*

NOTES

_____

_____

_____

_____

"Cooo - coo - cu .... cooo - coo - cu ....." Woodpigeon

Woodpigeon *(Columba palumbus)*

This large and omnipresent pigeon has become such an
integrated part of our landscape that he has now set up
home in our towns and parks, as well as our countryside.
Despite his reputation for spoiling farm crops, we forgive
him much on account of his soft and dreamy cooing song.
Consisting of five comforting muffled notes, this bird's song
has a depth and rhythm that is much loved, and because of
his long breeding season, he can often be heard long after the
other birds have ended their serenades. His song has led to
his Scottish nickname of 'Cushy-do'.

*The red stag that had paus'd to drink
Beside the rivulet's plashy brink,
Exhausted flings his dappled side
Along the clear, pellucid tide.
'Tis then the pigeons seek the wood
To roost, a swarming multitude.*
ISAAC MCLELLAN

June/July

Monday
30

Canada Day (Holiday CAN)

Tuesday
1

Wednesday
2

Thursday
3

Independence Day (Holiday USA)

Friday
4

Saturday
5

Sunday
6

July

Monday
7

Tuesday
8

Wednesday
9

Thursday
10

Friday
11

Saturday   Battle of the Boyne
12

Sunday
13

"Tcheer - tcheer.... tcheer.." Starling

Starling *(Sturnus vulgaris)*

NOTES

_____

_____

_____

_____

"Tcheer - tcheer..... tcheer.." Starling

Starling *(Sturnus vulgaris)*

Something of a tearaway, the starling has a song made up of
an assortment of mismatched squeaks, whistles and chuckles.
He often imitates other birds and is even known to imitate
the sound of a telephone ringing. This brash and cheeky
bird calls noisily with high-pitched squeaking before roosting
and is most admirable when seen in numbers. Winter flocks
containing thousands swoop and dive gracefully before settling
moments later in complete silence at their chosen destination.
The oily black feathers of the starling are shot with purple and
green and when flying together in vast numbers they create an
impressive black-cloud spectacle that is a sight not to be missed.

But I will find him when he lies asleep,
And in his ear I'll holla 'Mortimer!'
Nay, I'll have a starling shall be taught to speak
Nothing but 'Mortimer', and give it him,
To keep his anger still in motion.
WILLIAM SHAKESPEARE

July

Holiday (N. Ireland)

Monday
14

Tuesday
15

Wednesday
16

Thursday
17

Friday
18

Saturday
19

Sunday
20

July

Monday
21

Tuesday
22

Wednesday
23

Thursday
24

Friday
25

Saturday
26

Sunday
27

" Twit- twit... twit- twit...." Knot

Knot *(Calidris canuta)*

NOTES

_____

_____

_____

_____

_____

" Twit twit... twit-twit...." Knot

Knot *(Calidris canuta)*

The knot is a stocky, wading bird whose appearance changes
according to the seasons. In winter it is grey, with a white
belly, but in summer its chest and face become brick red,
almost like sunburn! In America it is known as a red knot
because of this lovely summer plumage. Few sights can
rival that of the huge flocks that twist and turn in the sky
in winter as they visit the UK from their Arctic breeding
grounds; it has been estimated that some of these wheeling
flocks contain in excess of 100,000 birds. Knots have a short,
deepish call, which fills the air as they swoop and circle.

On the clefts of the wave-washed rock I sit,
When the ocean is roaring and raving nigh;
On the howling tempest I scream and flit,
With the storm in my wing,
*   and the gale in my eye.*
JOHN GARDINER CALKINS BRAINARD

July/August

Monday
28

Tuesday
29

Wednesday
30

Thursday
31

Friday
1

Saturday
2

Sunday
3

August

Monday   Holiday (SCT, R. of Ireland)

4

Tuesday

5

Wednesday

6

Thursday

7

Friday

8

Saturday

9

Sunday

10

"Eeeee-airr......" Arctic Skua

Arctic Skua *(Stercorarius parasiticus)*

NOTES

"Eeeee - airr......." Arctic Skua

Arctic Skua *(Stercorarius parasiticus)*

This dark-looking seabird, also known as a parasitic jaeger in America, has the reputation of being an avian pirate, as it steals much of its food from other birds. It chases its fellow coastal birds, especially terns, high into the air in order to make them drop the fish they have caught for their own suppers! Arctic skuas spend most of their time at sea, and may not visit land for up to two years, until they are ready to breed. Once on land they can be very aggressive, dive-bombing anyone or anything that gets too close to their nests.

Bird of the briny deep!
Billow and storm,
Up from the darkness leap –
Wildly around thee sweep,
Terribly raging, while fearless thy form
Rides high on the froth of the skyward sea,
Where the winds and the waves, have revels for thee.
JOHN NELSON M'JILTON

August

Monday

11

Tuesday

12

Wednesday

13

Thursday

14

Friday

15

Saturday

16

Sunday

17

August

Monday
18

Tuesday
19

Wednesday
20

Thursday
21

Friday
22

Saturday
23

Sunday
24

"Kwarr- kwarrr ...." Black-headed Gull

Black-headed Gull *(Chroicocephalus ridibundus)*

NOTES

"Kwarr- kwarr ...." Black-headed Gull

Black-headed Gull *(Chroicocephalus ridibundus)*

This noisy, argumentative bird is mis-named, as for most of
the year it has a white head, which changes to dark brown,
not black, in the summer. It is actually quite a little gull, but
the noise it manages to create defies its small stature, and
it is certainly extremely bold in its search for insects, scraps
and carrion, both on the coast and further inland. It is quite
a sociable bird and gathers into larger parties where there is
plenty of food on offer. The black-headed gull is now a fairly
frequent visitor to urban gardens, particularly in cold winters,
when it is on the hunt for scraps of food.

Mountains and valleys of silver cloud,
Wherein to swing, sweep, soar,
A host of screeching, scolding, scrabbling
Sea-birds on the shore,
A snowy, silent, sun-washed drift
Of sea-birds on the shore.
WALTER DE LA MARE

August

Holiday (UK except SCT)

Monday

25

Tuesday

26

Wednesday

27

Thursday

28

Friday

29

Saturday

30

Sunday

31

September

Monday

Labor Day (Holiday USA)
Labour Day (Holiday CAN)

1

Tuesday

2

Wednesday

3

Thursday

4

Friday

5

Saturday

6

Sunday

Father's Day (AUS, NZL)

7

"Wi-choo wi-choo ...teechn"..... Coal Tit

Coal Tit *(Periparus ater)*

NOTES

_____

_____

_____

_____

"Wi-choo wi-choo ...teechu"..... Coal Tit

Coal Tit *(Periparus ater)*

The courting call of the smallest of the tits is soft and
repetitive and his song is high-pitched and bright.
This diminutive but friendly chap prefers to live amongst tall
coniferous trees. As the seasons become colder he takes on
a nomadic existence, often travelling in large flocks through
woods and gardens on a communal quest for food. He feasts
on tiny insects, nuts and seeds and sometimes stores his food
between the tufts of pine needles for a later meal. In spring
the female builds her moss and hair-lined nest in a tree cavity,
among tree stumps or ground burrows.

Once I saw a little bird
Come hop, hop, hop;
So I cried, 'Little bird,
Will you stop, stop, stop?'
And was going to the window
To say, 'How do you do?'
But he shook his little tail,
And far away he flew.
NURSERY RHYME

September

Monday
8

Tuesday
9

Wednesday
10

Thursday
11

Friday
12

Saturday
13

Sunday
14

September

Monday

15

Tuesday

16

Wednesday

17

Thursday

18

Friday

19

Saturday

20

Sunday   UN International Day of Peace

21

"Graa - graa..... kyarrr..."
Jackdaw

Jackdaw *(Corvus monedula)*

NOTES

Jackdaw *(Corvus monedula)*

The smallest of the crow family, the jackdaw is often seen in large flocks and is recognisable by his ash-grey hooded head, unusual pale grey eyes and a very jaunty, roguish swagger that only reinforces his reputation as a feathered bandit.

The jackdaw has a sharp, noisy monosyllabic yapping voice and while not a tuneful fellow, he makes up for this with an entertaining talent for mimicry that shows his inquisitive and intelligent nature. The name 'daw' has been used for this bird since the fifteenth century and is most likely derived, at least in part, from the sounds of its resonant call.

There is a bird who, by his coat
And by the hoarseness of his note,
Might be supposed a crow:
A great frequenter of the church,
Where, bishop-like, he finds a perch,
And dormitory too.
WILLIAM COWPER

September

Monday

22

Tuesday

23

Wednesday

24

Thursday

25

Friday

26

Saturday

27

Daylight Saving Time begins (NZL)

Sunday

28

September/October

WEEK 40

Monday
29

Tuesday
30

Wednesday
1

Thursday
2

Friday
3

Saturday
4

World Animal Day

Sunday
5

Daylight Saving Time begins
(AUS – except WA, NT, QLD)

"Quick- wee- wik........." Quail

Quail *(Coturnix coturnix)*

NOTES

_____

_____

_____

_____

"Quick - wee - wik........." Quail

Quail *(Coturnix coturnix)*

The petite quail can be resident or migratory and is most
common across the warmer parts of Southern Europe.
He keeps to himself and is hard to see because of his
reluctance to take to the skies. His nature is reclusive and
he is usually heard rather than seen.
He has a resonant, ventriloquist, call that can be thrown
far from its source, helping him maintain his privacy.
His song has three distinct syllables and has led to many
anthropomorphic translations such as 'Wet my lips' and
'Wet my foot'. Perhaps both of these have reinforced his
reputation as a prophet for the onset of rain.

When from my foot a bird did flee,
The rain flew bouncing from her breast
I wondered what the bird could be,
And almost trampled on her nest.
The nest was full of eggs and round,
I met a shepherd in the vales,
And stood to tell him what I found.
He knew and said it was a quail's.
JOHN CLARE

October

Monday
6

Tuesday
7

Wednesday
8

Thursday
9

Friday
10

Saturday
11

Sunday
12

October

Monday

Columbus Day (Holiday USA)
Thanksgiving Day (Holiday CAN)

13

Tuesday

14

Wednesday

15

Thursday

16

Friday

17

Saturday

18

Sunday

19

" Chit - chit - chiti - tzerrr........" Wren

Wren *(Troglodytes troglodytes)*

NOTES

" Chit - chit - chiti - tzerrr........" Wren

Wren *(Troglodytes troglodytes)*

A living adage to the saying that size is not everything, the diminutive wren is a most determined and impressive singer and his boisterous and full-throated warbling song can be heard loudly across the seasons. His song is shrill and is delivered with real gusto. One of Europe's smallest birds, the wren spends most of his time on or near the ground.
A sociable creature, it roosts in groups and is often found in gardens, woodland undergrowth or thickets beside ditches and streams. In spring, the male uses plant stalks, twigs and moss to build a number of spherical nests, the female takes her pick and the new home is finished inside with soft hair and feathers.

Among the dwelling framed by birds
In field or forest with nice care,
Is none that with the little Wren's
In snugness may compare.
WILLIAM WORDSWORTH

October

Monday
20

Tuesday
21

Wednesday
22

Thursday
23

Friday
24

Saturday
25

British Summer Time ends
European Daylight Saving Time ends

Sunday
26

October/November

Monday
27

Tuesday
28

Wednesday
29

Thursday
30

Friday
31

Hallowe'en

Saturday
1

Sunday
2

Daylight Saving Time ends (CAN, USA)

" Tzeee - tzeee ...... " Crested Tit

Crested Tit *(Lophophanes cristatus)*

NOTES

_____

_____

_____

_____

"Tzeee - tzeee ....." Crested Tit

Crested Tit *(Lophophanes cristatus)*

The crested tit can be found in pine forests and deciduous woods across mainland Europe and the Scottish Highlands in Great Britain. He is the proud owner of a tall, pointed, mottled, black and white head crest, which the male displays by spreading and closing his head crest feathers at times of courtship. This action is accompanied by a distinctive, if slightly stuttering, serenade and a number of endearing courtly bows to his female. Seemingly oblivious or unconcerned by people, he can happily be watched at close distance. The male builds his nest often utilising a disused squirrel's drey or excavating his own soft, cup-shaped abode in a decaying tree stump.

O for thy wings, sweet bird!
And soul of melody by being blest –
Like thee, my voice had stirred
Some dear remembrance in a weary breast.
But whither wouldst thou rove,
Bird of the airy wing, and fold thy plumes?
In what dark leafy grove
Wouldst chant thy vespers 'mid rich glooms?
MARY BAKER EDDY

November

Monday
3

Tuesday
4

Bonfire Night

Wednesday
5

Thursday
6

Friday
7

Saturday
8

Remembrance Sunday (UK)

Sunday
9

November

Monday
10

Tuesday
11

Remembrance Day (Holiday CAN)
Veterans' Day (Holiday USA)

Wednesday
12

Thursday
13

Friday
14

Saturday
15

Sunday
16

"Kcaaaa - Kcaaaw........." Rook

Rook *(Corvus frugilegus)*

NOTES

"Kcaaaa - Kcaaaw........." Rook

Rook *(Corvus frugilegus)*

The noisy cawing voice of this corvid (bird of the crow family) is raucous and resonant. Set at a similar pitch to that of a crying baby, it is an impossible call to miss. This large bird flourishes in areas of mixed farming and is most often heard en masse, chatting voraciously as they build their breeding colony of nests high up in the bare winter branches.

Glossy black in appearance, the rook is distinguished by his rather fluffy, thick black trouser feathers and the bare-faced patch at the base of his tapered bill.

Rook: Throughout the field I find no grain;
The cruel frost encrusts the cornland!
Starling: Aye: patient pecking now is vain
Throughout the field, I find…
Rook: No grain!
Pigeon: Nor will be, comrade, till it rain,
Or genial thawings loose the lorn land
Throughout the field.
THOMAS HARDY

November

Monday
17

Tuesday
18

Wednesday
19

Thursday
20

Friday
21

Saturday
22

Sunday
23

November

Monday
24

Tuesday
25

Wednesday
26

Thursday · Thanksgiving Day (Holiday USA)
27

Friday
28

Saturday
29

Sunday · St Andrew's Day
30

"Chek - chek... - chek...... chirrrr......" Garden Warbler

Garden Warbler *(Sylvia borin)*

NOTES

"Chek.. chek.. chek....chirrrr......" Garden Warbler

Garden Warbler *(Sylvia borin)*

Often praised as the virtuoso of the garden birds, the garden warbler is blessed with a remarkably musical and attractive song. Sometimes confused with the voice of the blackcap, this fellow appears to warble at length without drawing breath and produces an almost clarinet-like pure quality of tone that is loud, rich and brilliant. Perhaps surprisingly, this musical maestro is rather plainly dressed in greyish brown plumage with dull buff underparts and was only identified at the end of the eighteenth century. He is less visible than one might expect from such an exuberant songster and builds his shallow nest in low thickets or fruit bushes that are adeptly concealed.

Sing, little birdie, sing
On topmost branches high!
And when thou spreadst thy airy wing,
Let not the sweet notes die,
But longer, louder be,
Until the echoes ring
That hide away where none may see,
But only hear them sing.
WATIE W. SWANZY

December

Monday

1

Tuesday

2

Wednesday

3

Thursday

4

Friday

5

Saturday

6

Sunday

7

December

Monday
8

Tuesday
9

Wednesday
10

Thursday
11

Friday
12

Saturday
13

Sunday
14

"Weeet - sac - tsacct...........'' Stonechat

Stonechat *(Saxicola torquata)*

NOTES

"Weeet - sac - tsacct........." Stonechat

Stonechat *(Saxicola torquata)*

The call of the stonechat has often been compared to the
noise made by two stones being knocked together, and
it is likely that this is how he was christened. His rather
diminutive song is a chattering, grating warble and he saves a
harsh scolding call for moments of alarm.

He is well dressed with a black head, crisp white half collar
and a robust russet-red chest. These distinct markings and his
preference for perching high aloft on telegraph wires or on
the crowns of gorse bushes make him an easy bird to spot.

*Stranger! these gloomy boughs
Had charms for him; and here he
    loved to sit,
His only visitants a straggling sheep,
The stone-chat, or the glancing
    sand-piper…*
WILLIAM WORDSWORTH

December

Monday
15

Tuesday
16

Wednesday
17

Thursday
18

Friday
19

Saturday
20

Sunday
21

December

Monday

22

Tuesday

23

Wednesday

24

Christmas Eve

Thursday

25

Christmas Day
(Holiday UK, R. of Ireland, USA, CAN, AUS, NZL)

Friday

26

Boxing Day, St Stephen's Day
(Holiday UK, R. of Ireland, CAN, AUS, NZL)

Saturday

27

Sunday

28

December 2014/January 2015

Monday

29

Tuesday

30

New Year's Eve

Wednesday

31

New Year's Day
(Holiday UK, R. of Ireland, USA, CAN, AUS, NZL)

Thursday

1

Holiday (SCT, NZL)

Friday

2

Saturday

3

Sunday

4

2015 Planner

JANUARY		FEBRUARY		MARCH	
1	T	1	S	1	S
2	F	2	M	2	M
3	S	3	T	3	T
4	S	4	W	4	W
5	M	5	T	5	T
6	T	6	F	6	F
7	W	7	S	7	S
8	T	8	S	8	S
9	F	9	M	9	M
10	S	10	T	10	T
11	S	11	W	11	W
12	M	12	T	12	T
13	T	13	F	13	F
14	W	14	S	14	S
15	T	15	S	15	S
16	F	16	M	16	M
17	S	17	T	17	T
18	S	18	W	18	W
19	M	19	T	19	T
20	T	20	F	20	F
21	W	21	S	21	S
22	T	22	S	22	S
23	F	23	M	23	M
24	S	24	T	24	T
25	S	25	W	25	W
26	M	26	T	26	T
27	T	27	F	27	F
28	W	28	S	28	S
29	T			29	S
30	F			30	M
31	S			31	T

APRIL		MAY		JUNE	
1	W	1	F	1	M
2	T	2	S	2	T
3	F	3	S	3	W
4	S	4	M	4	T
5	S	5	T	5	F
6	M	6	W	6	S
7	T	7	T	7	S
8	W	8	F	8	M
9	T	9	S	9	T
10	F	10	S	10	W
11	S	11	M	11	T
12	S	12	T	12	F
13	M	13	W	13	S
14	T	14	T	14	S
15	W	15	F	15	M
16	T	16	S	16	T
17	F	17	S	17	W
18	S	18	M	18	T
19	S	19	T	19	F
20	M	20	W	20	S
21	T	21	T	21	S
22	W	22	F	22	M
23	T	23	S	23	T
24	F	24	S	24	W
25	S	25	M	25	T
26	S	26	T	26	F
27	M	27	W	27	S
28	T	28	T	28	S
29	W	29	F	29	M
30	T	30	S	30	T
		31	S		

2015 Planner

JULY	AUGUST	SEPTEMBER
1 W	1 S	1 T
2 T	2 S	2 W
3 F	3 M	3 T
4 S	4 T	4 F
5 S	5 W	5 S
6 M	6 T	6 S
7 T	7 F	7 M
8 W	8 S	8 T
9 T	9 S	9 W
10 F	10 M	10 T
11 S	11 T	11 F
12 S	12 W	12 S
13 M	13 T	13 S
14 T	14 F	14 M
15 W	15 S	15 T
16 T	16 S	16 W
17 F	17 M	17 T
18 S	18 T	18 F
19 S	19 W	19 S
20 M	20 T	20 S
21 T	21 F	21 M
22 W	22 S	22 T
23 T	23 S	23 W
24 F	24 M	24 T
25 S	25 T	25 F
26 S	26 W	26 S
27 M	27 T	27 S
28 T	28 F	28 M
29 W	29 S	29 T
30 T	30 S	30 W
31 F	31 M	

2015 Planner

OCTOBER	NOVEMBER	DECEMBER
1 T	1 S	1 T
2 F	2 M	2 W
3 S	3 T	3 T
4 S	4 W	4 F
5 M	5 T	5 S
6 T	6 F	6 S
7 W	7 S	7 M
8 T	8 S	8 T
9 F	9 M	9 W
10 S	10 T	10 T
11 S	11 W	11 F
12 M	12 T	12 S
13 T	13 F	13 S
14 W	14 S	14 M
15 T	15 S	15 T
16 F	16 M	16 W
17 S	17 T	17 T
18 S	18 W	18 F
19 M	19 T	19 S
20 T	20 F	20 S
21 W	21 S	21 M
22 T	22 S	22 T
23 F	23 M	23 W
24 S	24 T	24 T
25 S	25 W	25 F
26 M	26 T	26 S
27 T	27 F	27 S
28 W	28 S	28 M
29 T	29 S	29 T
30 F	30 M	30 W
31 S		31 T

Names & Addresses

Name

Address

Postcode

Telephone   Mobile

E-mail

Name

Address

Postcode

Telephone   Mobile

E-mail

Name

Address

Postcode

Telephone   Mobile

E-mail

Name

Address

Postcode

Telephone   Mobile

E-mail

Name

Address

Postcode

Telephone   Mobile

E-mail

Name

Address

Postcode

Telephone   Mobile

E-mail

Names & Addresses

Name

Address

Postcode

Telephone   Mobile

E-mail

Name

Address

Postcode

Telephone   Mobile

E-mail

Name

Address

Postcode

Telephone   Mobile

E-mail

Name

Address

Postcode

Telephone   Mobile

E-mail

Name

Address

Postcode

Telephone   Mobile

E-mail

Name

Address

Postcode

Telephone   Mobile

E-mail

Names & Addresses

Name

Address

Postcode

Telephone   Mobile

E-mail

Name

Address

Postcode

Telephone   Mobile

E-mail

Name

Address

Postcode

Telephone   Mobile

E-mail

Name

Address

Postcode

Telephone   Mobile

E-mail

Name

Address

Postcode

Telephone   Mobile

E-mail

Name

Address

Postcode

Telephone   Mobile

E-mail

Names & Addresses

Name

Address

Postcode

Telephone　　　　　　　　　　　Mobile

E-mail

Name

Address

Postcode

Telephone　　　　　　　　　　　Mobile

E-mail

Name

Address

Postcode

Telephone　　　　　　　　　　　Mobile

E-mail

Name

Address

Postcode

Telephone　　　　　　　　　　　Mobile

E-mail

Name

Address

Postcode

Telephone　　　　　　　　　　　Mobile

E-mail

Name

Address

Postcode

Telephone　　　　　　　　　　　Mobile

E-mail

Notes

Notes

Notes